Fun With Daffodil Duck

Activities by Maida Silverman
Illustrated by Maryann Cocca-Leffler

PlayValue Books™
A Division of Grosset & Dunlap

ABC DEFGHIJ

How to Use this Book

Spring is here! And Daffodil Duck and her friends Little Chick and Buttercup Lamb have figured out lots of good springtime puzzles for you to do. For most of the activities, all you need are crayons or a pencil. A few of the projects call for special supplies, like scissors or glue.

For extra fun, play the magic daffodil trick (on page 44), or try making Daffodil Duck's special bookmarks (page 41). There are even instructions (on page 24) for making your very own Easter bonnet.

Now, find your crayons and pencils, and get ready to have a good time!

A Fine Spring Morning
a picture to color

Daffodil Duck lives at the edge of the pond.

What a Crazy Farm!

Little Chick can see six strange things happening in the barnyard. Can you find them, too? *(The answers to the puzzles begin on page 46.)*

It's Daffodil Time

Cut out the puzzle pieces along the outside lines. Fit the pieces together. Then you will see Daffodil Duck doing one of her favorite chores.

Cut out the puzzle
on the other side
of the page.

What a Sunny Day!

Connect the dots to find out what Daffodil wears when the sun is bright.

Are the Pictures Alike?

Only two of the pictures of Buttercup Lamb are exactly the same. Draw a circle around the two that are alike.

8

R Is for Rooster

Can you find seven things in the picture that being with R—not counting Farmer Rooster?

Climb on the Tractor
a picture to color

Farmer Rooster takes Little Chick for a ride.

Something Doesn't Belong Here!

One picture in each row doesn't belong with the others. Circle the pictures that are different.

Which Way?

Daffodil Duck wants to meet Little Chick on the other side of the big vegetable garden. Can you help Daffodil get there—without stepping on any vegetables?

Daffodil's Baking Day

The six pictures below are not in the right order. Cut out the pictures, and then arrange them so that they show how Daffodil Duck bakes chocolate-chip cookies.

Cut out the puzzle
on the other side
of the page.

Who Said That?

Draw a line from each animal to the sound that it makes.

Oink!

Quack!

Woof!

Meow!

Moo!

Neigh!

It's a Daisy-chain Day
a picture to color

The meadow is Buttercup Lamb's favorite spot.

A Pond Puzzle

Daffodil Duck wants to swim home to her little house, but the water lilies are blocking her way. Can you show Daffodil a clear path to her house?

START

A Ridiculous Day in the Kitchen

Little Chick is helping Mama Hen make lemonade, but there are six silly things happening here. Can you find all six?

What Is Daffodil Doing?

Daffodil Duck is having a good time. To find out what is going on here, just connect the dots.

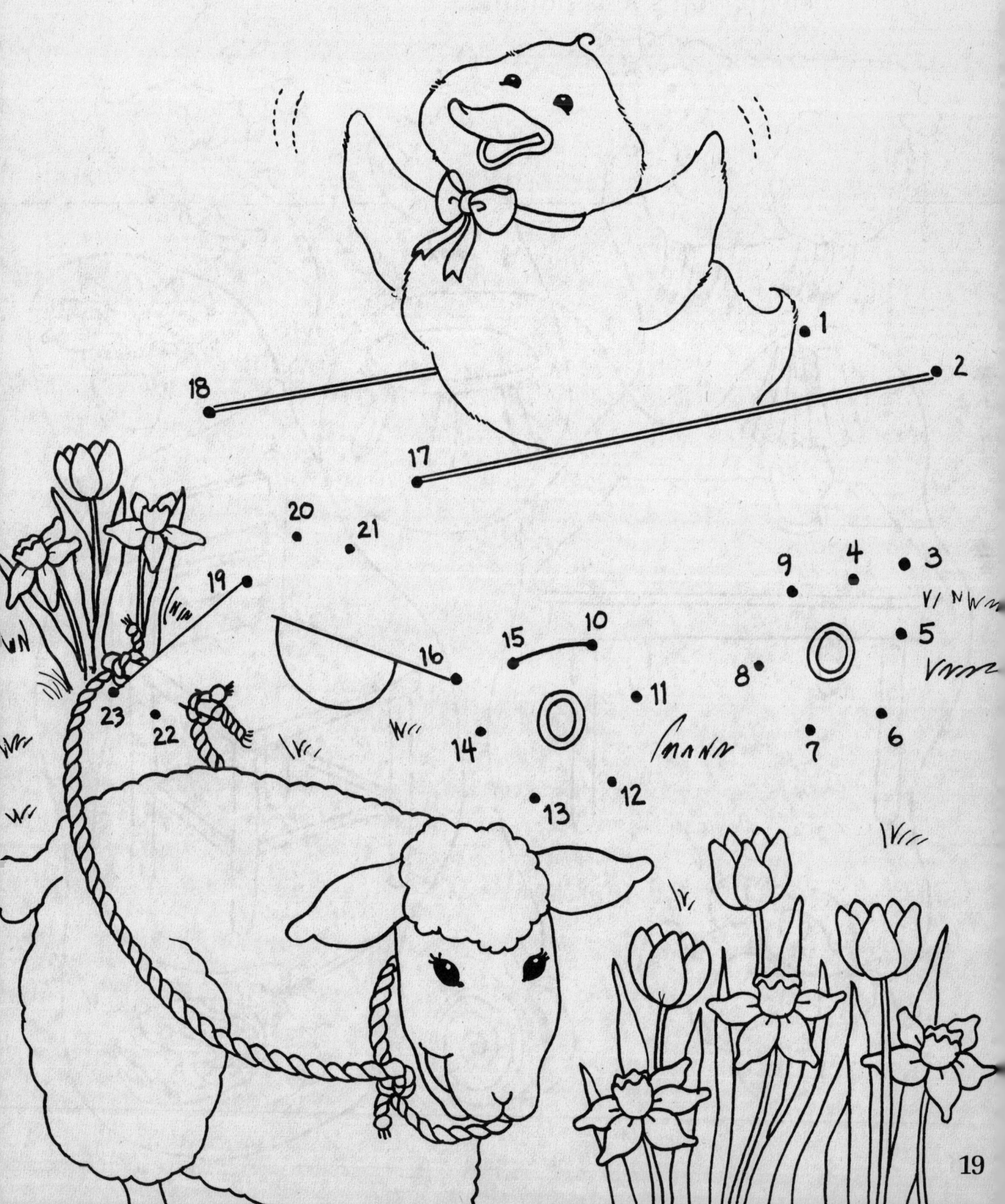

What Will Daffodil Win?

To find out what Daffodil Duck's prize will be at the end of the treasure hunt, just follow the string that she is holding.

What Does the Artist Need?

Daffodil Duck is going to paint a picture of the spring flowers. Circle five things on the table that she will need to complete her painting.

What Shall We Do Today?

One rainy day, [chick] was visiting [sheep] .

After a while, [chick] looked out the [window] .

The [rain cloud] had stopped, and the [sun] was

shining. "It's a nice day now," said

[chick] . "What shall we do on this [sun]

afternoon?" said [sheep] . Just then, there

was a knock at the [door] . Surprise!

It was [duck] holding a big [basket] . "Let's

all go pick wild [strawberries] this afternoon,"

she said. "Wonderful!" said [sheep] . "And

for dessert tonight," said [chick] , "we'll

have [cake] ! Let's go!"

New Clothes For Easter
a picture to color

Mrs. Hen has just finished sewing Little Chick's
new Easter outfit.

It's Easter-bonnet Time!

You can make a pretty flowered hat like the one Daffodil is wearing.

You will need:
a paper plate, white or colored
a paper doily (optional)
2 ribbons, about 16" long each
scissors
glue

How to make:
1. Color and cut the flowers on the opposite page. (If you want more flowers for your hat, draw and color more blossoms on blank paper and cut out.)
2. Paste the doily to the bottom of the paper plate. (Optional)
3. Paste the flowers on top of the doily or on top of the upside-down plate.
4. Ask an adult to make a hole for you on each side of the hat. Tie a ribbon through each hole—and your hat is ready to wear!

Cut out the flowers
on the other side
of the page.

Who Gave a Gift?

Who left jellybeans for Buttercup Lamb? To find out, write a letter under each picture on the card. The code below will tell you what letter to write under the pictures.

To Buttercup Lamb from:

_ _ _ _ _ _ _ _

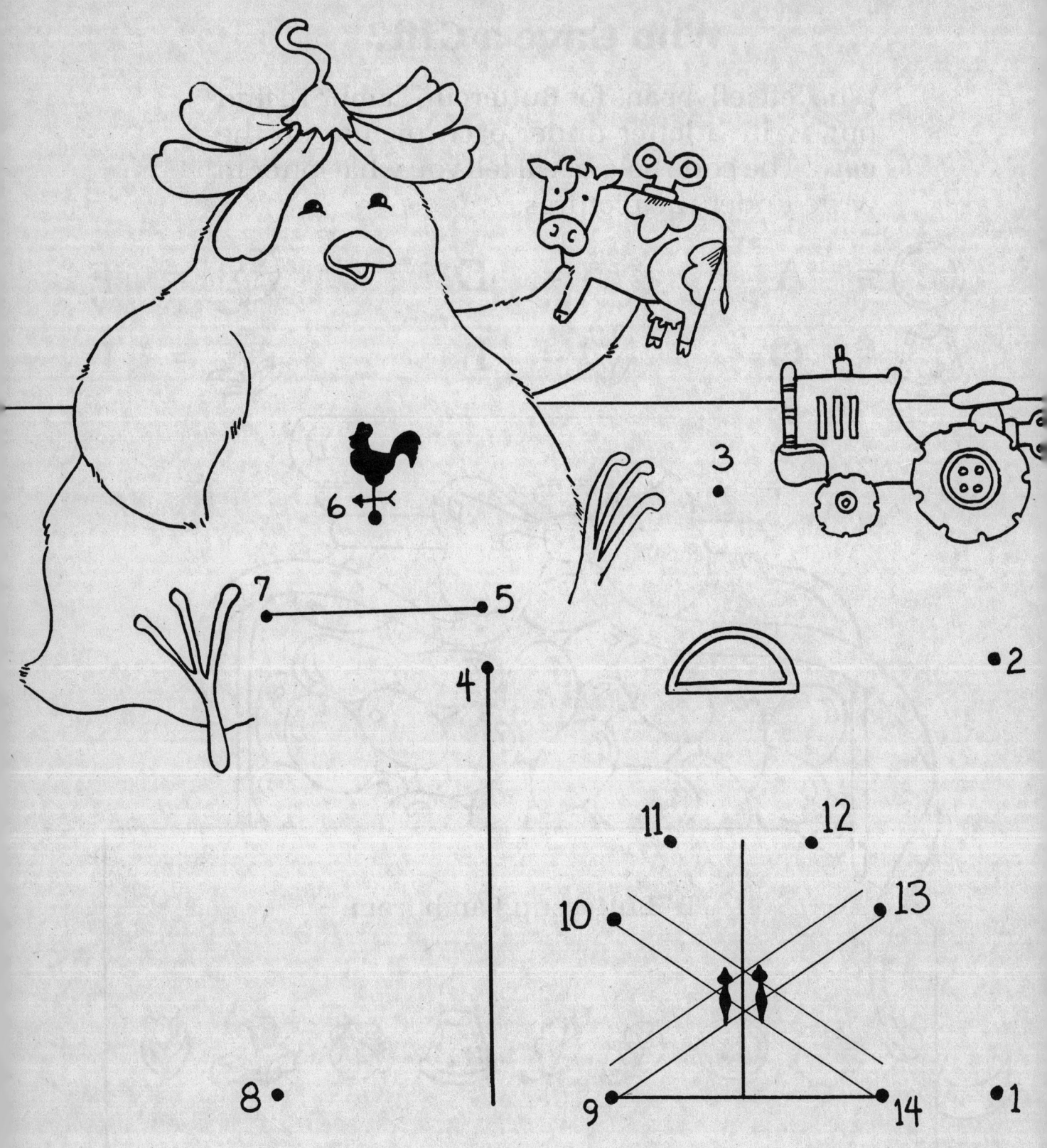

It's Playtime!

What is Little Chick playing with? To find out, just connect the dots.

Who Can Fly?

Only six of these animals and insects can fly.
Can you find all six?

What's on the Roof?

Farmer Rooster has built something interesting.
To find out what it is, color each space that has a
dot in it.

The Silliest Picnic Ever!

Little Chick and her parents are having a picnic under the willow tree. Can you find six things wrong in the picture?

Daffodil Duck's Shoe Hunt

Daffodil is trying to neaten her closet. Show her which shoes go together by drawing a line between each matching pair. There are six pairs in all.

What's In the Barn?

Can you find each of the following eight objects hidden inside the barn?

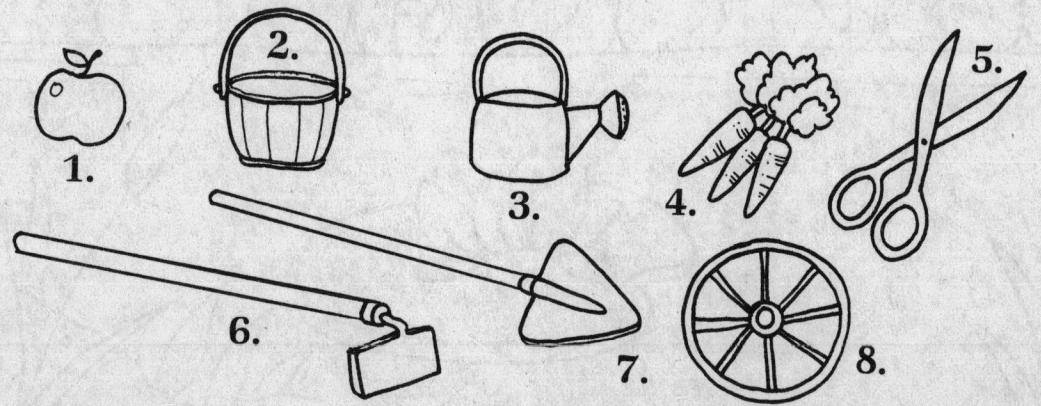

1.
2.
3.
4.
5.
6.
7.
8.

Windy Day at the Pond
a picture to color

What a good day to go sailing!

A Mysterious Message

To read the friendly message that Little Chick has left for you, draw a line between each pair of matching flowers. Draw four lines in all.

All Fenced In

Buttercup Lamb can't find his way to the barn. Show him a clear path through the fences so that he can visit Little Chick.

END

START

Don't Get Wet!

Little Chick is going out for a walk in the rain. Circle the four things Little Chick will need so that she can stay dry.

D Is for Duck

Can you find six things in the picture that start with D—not counting Daffodil Duck?

A Trip to the Florist

To find out which kind of flower Buttercup Lamb wants to buy, figure out the name of each object below. Then write the first letter of each word in the space next to the picture—and the letters will spell the name of a flower!

An Egg Puzzle

Four little chicks have just hatched from their eggs. Draw a line from each half of an egg to the half that fits it.

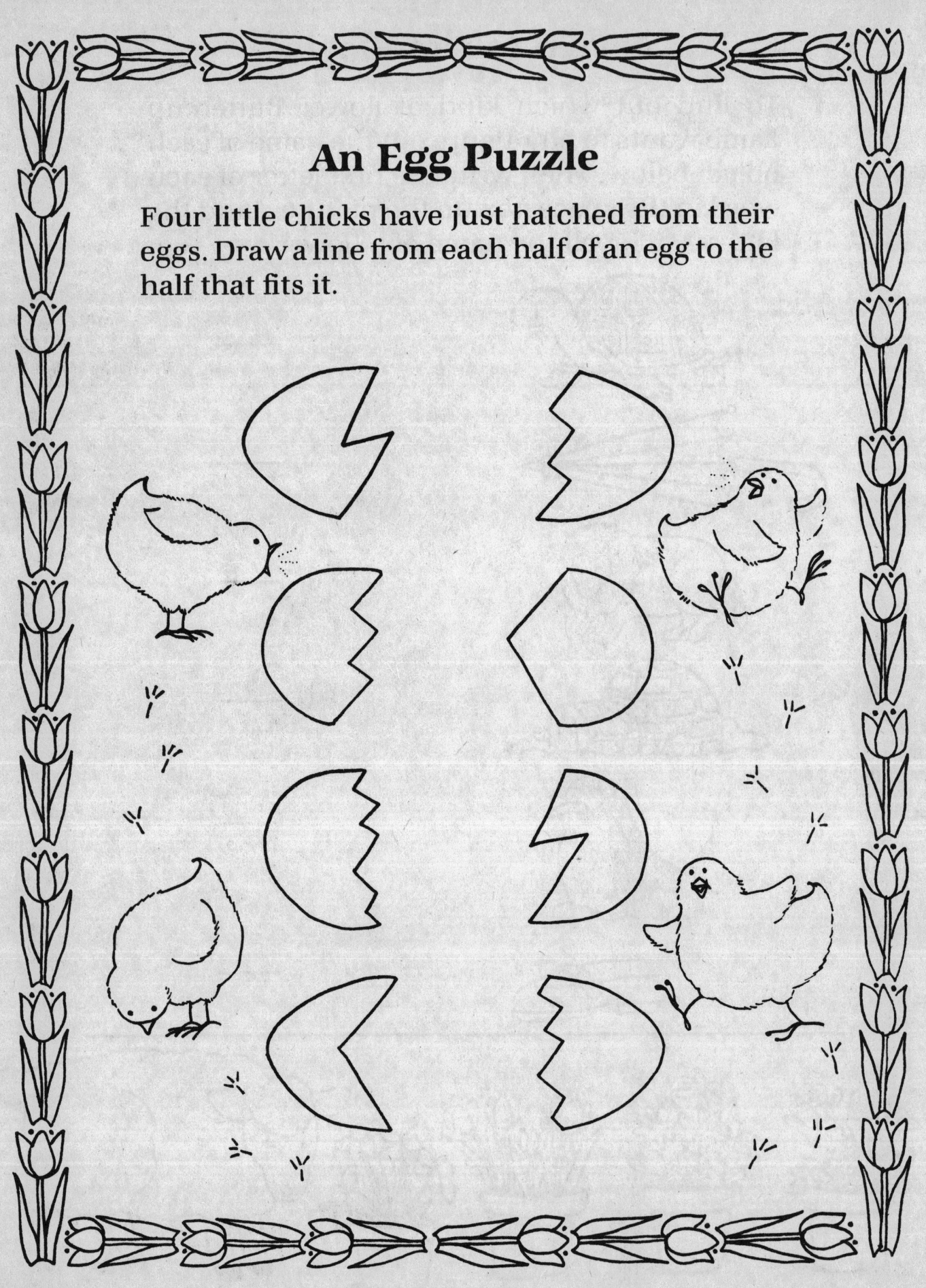

40

Make Your Own Bookmarks

Color the three bookmarks. Then paste them onto heavy paper and cut them out along the dotted lines. Daffodil and her friends will help you keep your place—in any book you choose!

Cut out the bookmarks
on the other side
of the page.

How Many Butterflies?

There are eight butterflies hidden in the picture. Color the butterflies, and then color the rest of the picture.

A Magic Trick!

Daffodil Duck can turn ten daffodils into five—
without taking any of them off the table. Cut out
the daffodil pictures and see if you can do the
magic trick, too!

Good-bye for Now
a picture to color

What a nice spring day this has been!

ANSWERS

page 4
WHAT A CRAZY FARM!

page 5
IT'S DAFFODIL TIME

page 8
ARE THE PICTURES ALIKE?

page 9
R IS FOR ROOSTER

rope	rose
rain	rabbit
rug	roller skates
ribbon	

page 11
SOMETHING DOESN'T BELONG HERE!

page 12
WHICH WAY?

page 13
DAFFODIL'S BAKING DAY

page 15
WHO SAID THAT?

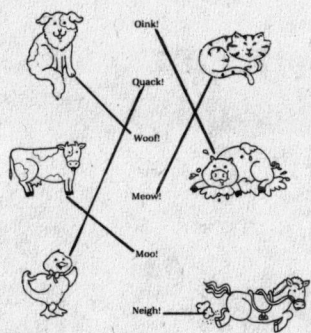

page 17
A POND PUZZLE

page 18
A RIDICULOUS DAY
IN THE KITCHEN

page 21
WHAT DOES THE ARTIST
NEED?

paints   big brush
water   small brush
paper

page 27
WHO GAVE A GIFT?

Answer: DAFFODIL

page 29
WHO CAN FLY?

butterfly   seagull
blue jay   dragonfly
bat   bee

page 31
THE SILLIEST PICNIC EVER!

page 32
DAFFODIL DUCK'S SHOE HUNT

page 33
WHAT'S IN THE BARN?

page 36
ALL FENCED IN

page 37
DON'T GET WET!

raincoat   boots
umbrella   rain hat

page 38
D IS FOR DUCK

daffodils   door
dice   dress
dog   desk

page 39
A TRIP TO THE FLORIST

Answer: tulips

page 40
AN EGG PUZZLE

page 43
HOW MANY BUTTERFLIES?

page 44
A MAGIC TRICK!

48